WILLIAM SHAKESP

Macbeth

Text adaption, notes and activities
by James Butler and Maria Lucia De Vanna

Editors: Rebecca Raynes, Elvira Poggi Repetto
Design: Nadia Maestri
Illustrations: Gianni De Conno

First edition: March 1999

5   4   3   2   1

We would be happy to receive your comments and suggestions, and give you any other information concerning our material.
Our address and fax number are:
Cideb Editrice – Piazza Garibaldi 11/2 – 16035 Rapallo (GE)
Fax 0185/230100 – e-mail: cidebedi@rapallo.newnetworks.it

PRINTED ON FREELIFE®FEDRIGONI

ISBN: 88-7754-480-5

Printed in Italy by Litoprint, Genoa

Contents

This story is recorded in full on the cassette.

𝔖𝔥𝔞𝔨𝔢𝔰𝔭𝔢𝔞𝔯𝔢'𝔰 𝔏𝔦𝔣𝔢

illiam Shakespeare was born in Stratford-upon-Avon, in April, 1564. The exact date of his birth is not known, but there is a tradition that it was the 23rd of April, which is St. George's Day – St. George is the patron saint of England.

William Shakespeare's father was an important man in Stratford-upon-Avon. He was a glove merchant by profession, and he became the town mayor. [1]

Little is known about the kind of schooling Shakespeare received as a boy, although it is likely he attended the Grammar School in his town, where boys were instructed in Latin.

At the age of eighteen William Shakespeare married Anne

The house in Stratford-upon-Avon where Shakespeare was born.

---

1. **mayor** [meər] : person elected to represent a city or town for a fixed period of time.

Hathaway, who was eight years older than himself. They had three children; a daughter Susan, and the twins Hamnet and Judith.

At some point after his marriage the young Shakespeare went to London, where he became involved in a theatrical company, the 'Lord Chamberlain's Men', at first as an actor and then as a writer of plays. As well as writing poetry, Shakespeare wrote thirty-eight plays, including histories, comedies, 'Roman plays' and tragedies. Shakespeare's work was gathered [1] together and published after his death. In 1599 Shakespeare's company built the Globe Theatre in London. The 'Lord Chamberlain's Men' became the 'King's Men' in 1603, and received protection from James I. The principal theatre of the 'King's Men' was the Blackfriars, from 1609 onwards.

The Globe Theatre in an early 17th-century drawing.

In 1610 William Shakespeare returned to Stratford-upon-Avon, where he died on the 23rd of April 1616.

Visitors to Stratford-upon-Avon can see the house where William Shakespeare was born, Anne Hathaway's cottage, and the Royal Shakespeare Theatre.

1. **gathered** : collected.

Answer the following questions.

a. In what year was Shakespeare born?
☐ 1524
☐ 1546
☐ 1564
☐ 1516

b. How old was Shakespeare when he married Anne Hathaway?
☐ 16
☐ 25
☐ 18
☐ 21

c. How many plays did Shakespeare write?
☐ 25
☐ 28
☐ 32
☐ 38

d. When was Shakespeare's work first published?
☐ when he became famous
☐ after his death
☐ when he moved to London
☐ after he got married

e. Which theatre did Shakespeare's company build?
☐ the Globe
☐ the Blackfriars
☐ the Royal Shakespeare

Shakespeare's Macbeth

Macbeth was probably written in 1606, and performed at the Globe Theatre in the same year. It is the shortest but one of the most powerful of Shakespeare's tragedies.

The main character of the play is Macbeth. At the beginning of the play he is shown as a conventional hero. He saves Scotland and the Scottish King Duncan from the army of the King of Norway and the rebellious Thane of Cawdor. After the battle Macbeth and his friend Banquo meet three witches. The witches tell Macbeth that he will first become the Thane of Cawdor, and then king. They tell Banquo that his children's children will be Kings. Macbeth begins to dream of ambition. He realises that he would like to be king, but he is afraid.

The murder of the King,
by Henry Fuseli.

Frontispiece to Macbeth, *from an 18th-century edition.*

Lady Macbeth encourages her husband to be ambitious. It is she who plans to murder Duncan when he comes to stay at the castle. Although Macbeth agrees to commit the murder, he is unhappy. Before the crime he imagines that he can see a dagger covered in blood in front of him; and after the crime he imagines that he can hear a voice crying 'Macbeth has murdered sleep – Macbeth will sleep no more'. His wife is impatient with his fears, and when he shows her the King's blood on his hands, she tells him that a little water will clean the blood away.

Once he has killed the King, Macbeth feels unsafe. He remembers that the witches have said that Banquo's family will become kings. He decides to murder Banquo. He is horrified when Banquo's ghost appears at a feast. Macbeth consults the witches again. They tell him to be careful of Macduff.

The banquet scene by Daniel Haclise.

Ellen Terry as Lady Macbeth, portrait by John Singer Sargent.

They also tell him that 'no man born of woman' can kill him, and that he will never be defeated 'until Birnam Wood comes to Dunsinane Hill'. Macbeth believes these predictions. He sends men to Macduff's castle with orders to kill Macduff. When the murderers arrive, Macduff has left the castle and gone to England. Macbeth's men kill Lady Macduff and her children.

The relationship between Macbeth and his wife changes in the second half of the play. His wife is now the one to suffer from guilt at what they have done – she is tormented by the thought of the blood on her hands.

Duncan's son, Malcolm, persuades Macduff to fight against Macbeth. Macduff joins them because he wants revenge for the murder of his wife and children. During the battle Macbeth realises that the witches have lied to him. He discovers that Macduff is the man 'not born of woman' who has the power to kill him, and he sees Birnam Wood come to Dunsinane Hill. Although he knows that he will now die, Macbeth decides to fight rather than be taken prisoner by Macduff.

Dramatis Personae

Duncan	King of Scotland
Malcolm	
Donalblain	his sons
Macbeth	Thane of Glamis, later of Cawdor, later King of Scotland
Banquo	
Macduff	
Lennox	Thanes of Scotland
Ross	

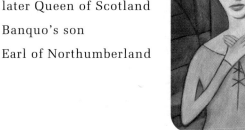

Lady Macbeth	later Queen of Scotland
Fleance	Banquo's son
Seyward	Earl of Northumberland
Porter of Macbeth's castle	
Doctor	
Young Seyward	
Three witches	
Hecate	Goddess of the witches
Three murderers	

PART ONE

Macbeth and the Witches

Duncan, the King of Scotland, was a good king, who was liked by most of his lords, or thanes. [1] The Thane of Cawdor, however, wanted to kill Duncan and become king. He asked the King of Norway to come to Scotland with a great army. [2]

At first everything went well for the King of Norway and the Thane of Cawdor. Their army was strong, and they had some victories against the Scottish.

Then King Duncan's army fought against the army of the King of Norway and the Thane of Cawdor. There was a desperate battle to save Scotland.

1. **thanes** : in Anglo-Saxon times thanes were barons to the King of Scotland.
2. **army** : organised group of soldiers.

Macbeth and the Witches

One of Duncan's loyal thanes was called Macbeth. He was Thane of Glamis. Macbeth fought very hard in the battle against the Thane of Cawdor, and he defeated the enemy. Duncan was very pleased with Macbeth, and wanted to reward [1] him for his loyalty. He called one of his Thanes.

'Ross,' Duncan said, 'I want you to do something for me. I have decided to execute [2] the Thane of Cawdor because he is a rebel who tried to kill me and become king. I want you to go to Macbeth, and to tell him that he will be the new Thane of Cawdor. It is my reward to him for his courage and loyalty.'

'Yes, sir,' said Ross. 'I'll go immediately and tell Macbeth.'

Macbeth and his friend, Banquo, were both tired after the battle. They were walking together, and they were talking about the events of the day. They were both excited and pleased that Duncan had won the battle. Suddenly Banquo stopped.

'Look!' he cried. 'Look at them!'

Macbeth looked, and saw in front of them three very strange figures. It was difficult to tell if they were men or women. They looked like old women, but they had beards and they were very ugly. They were standing around a fire, and there was a cooking-pot on it. There was a horrible smell coming from the cooking-pot.

'Are you women, or are you spirits?' [3] Banquo asked them.

'Answer him,' Macbeth said. 'Are you women or are you spirits?'

The first witch [4] looked at Macbeth, and said,

'Welcome Macbeth, Thane of Glamis.'

The second witch looked at Macbeth, and said,

'Welcome, Macbeth, Thane of Cawdor.'

---

1. **reward** : give a recompense in return for service or merit.
2. **execute** : kill as a punishment.
3. **spirits** : phantoms or ghosts.
4. **witch** : usually a woman with evil magic powers.

Macbeth

The third witch looked at Macbeth, and said to him,
'Welcome, Macbeth, King of Scotland.'

Macbeth was very surprised at what the three witches had told him, and he did not say anything. Banquo then asked the witches a question.

'You tell my friend that he will be Thane of Cawdor, and then King of Scotland, but you say nothing to me. If you can really see into the future, tell us something about my future. What will happen to me?'

Macbeth and the Witches

One of the witches replied,
'You will be less than Macbeth, but more than Macbeth.'
The second witch told him,
'You will be less lucky than Macbeth, but you will be more fortunate.'
The third witch told Banquo,
'You will never be king, but your children's children will be kings.'
After making these predictions, the witches suddenly disappeared.

Macbeth

'It's very strange!' Macbeth said to Banquo. 'They say that I will be Thane of Cawdor, and then king – and your children's children will be kings! I don't believe it, though. I don't know who they are, or what they are, but what they say makes no sense.'

'I don't know what to think,' said Banquo. 'Perhaps – '

Just as Banquo was speaking, Ross appeared.

'I have come from King Duncan,' he told Macbeth. 'I have a message for you from the King. He wants to reward you because he is very pleased with your courage and loyalty. He gave me a message to bring to you. You are the new Thane of Cawdor.'

Macbeth and Banquo looked at each other in astonishment. [1]

'The witches told the truth!' Macbeth said to Banquo.

'Be careful, my friend,' Banquo replied. 'They also told you that you'd be king, but perhaps the witches were bad spirits. I have heard that such spirits try to make men do wicked [2] things by making them promises.'

Macbeth said nothing to his friend, but he could not stop thinking about what the witches had said. He had always been loyal to Duncan, but now he began to question his loyalty for the first time. 'The witches told the truth,' he thought. 'They said I would be Thane of Cawdor, and now I *am* Thane of Cawdor. Perhaps I'll also be king one day!' He was excited about the idea of becoming king, but he was also frightened. 'I want to be king,' he thought, 'but Duncan is my friend – I don't want to hurt him.'

---

1. **astonishment** : great surprise.
2. **wicked** [wɪkɪd] : bad.

Comprehension

1 **Answer the following questions.**

    a. Why is the King pleased with Macbeth?

    b. How does Duncan reward Macbeth?

    c. Describe the three witches.

    d. What do the three witches tell Macbeth and Banquo? Complete the chart below.

They tell Macbeth:	They tell Banquo:

    e. What advice does Banquo give Macbeth about the witches?

    f. What does Macbeth think about the witches?

Vocabulary

2 **Complete these sentences, using words from the text.**

    a. Duncan was the .... of ....

    b. The Scottish lords were called ....

    c. The King of Norway led an .... into Scotland.

    d. There was a desperate .... to .... Scotland.

    e. The witches looked like old women, but they had ....

3 Put the words below into the appropriate column. Some of them have been done for you. Use a dictionary for words you do not know.

castle   magic   throne   soldiers   spell   battle
wicked   palace   predict   fight   reign
charm   defeat   march

King	Army	Witch

Grammar

Past Simple and Past Continuous

We often use the Past Continuous together with the Past Simple. The Past Continuous refers to an action that was in progress at a definite time in the past, and the Past Simple refers to a shorter action or event that happened in the middle of the longer action, or that interrupted it.

In the text you read:

They **were walking** together, and they **were talking** about the events of the day. They were both excited and pleased that Duncan had won the battle. Suddenly Banquo **stopped**.

4 **Put the verbs in brackets into the Past Simple or the Past Continuous.**

a. I .... *(sing)* when I .... *(hear)* a terrible noise.

b. A flower-pot .... *(fall)* from the window-sill and .... *(hit)* a dog that .... *(pass)* by.

c. Mary and I .... *(chat)* in the office the other day when the phone .... *(ring)*. It .... *(be)* my boss.

   She .... *(tell)* me: 'You .... *(come)* here this morning to work, not to chat!'

d. As I .... *(walk)* down the street, I .... *(see)* an old man. He was interesting because he .... *(ask)* people for money, although he .... *(wear)* very smart clothes.

e. My sister .... *(meet)* John when she .... *(work)* in London.

f. The dog .... *(bite)* me while I .... *(try)* to pick it up.

Listening

 5 **After you listen to Part One of *Macbeth* on the cassette you will hear two short extracts from the original Shakespeare. However, before you listen read them and try to fill in the gaps with the words from the box. Then listen and check your answers.**

> speak   Thane   greater   happier
> Cawdor   Banquo   king   hail

Extract One

Macbeth *(to the witches)*: Speak if you can! What are you?

First Witch: All hail, [1] Macbeth! Hail to thee, [2] .... of Glamis!

Second Witch: All hail, Macbeth. Hail to thee, Thane of ....!

Third Witch: All hail, Macbeth, that shalt be .... hereafter! [3]

1. **hail** : welcome.
2. **thee** : you.
3. **hereafter** : after this time.

Extract Two

Banquo: .... then to me, who neither beg [1] nor fear
   Your favours, [2] nor your hate.

First Witch: Hail!

Second Witch: Hail!

Third Witch: ....!

First Witch: Lesser than Macbeth, and ....

Second Witch: Not so happy, yet much ....

Third Witch: Thou shalt get [3] kings, though thou be none.
   So all hail, Macbeth, and ....!

Writing

6 Imagine you are Banquo. You are writing to a friend telling him/her about the three witches. Describe what the three witches look like, and say what they told you about your future.

....

....

....

....

....

....

Speaking

7 People in Shakespeare's time believed in witches and in the power of magic. They thought witches could tell the future. Nowadays, some people say they can tell the future by looking at a horoscope, or by examining a hand. What do you think of this kind of 'magic'?

1. **beg** : ask.
2. **favours** : good services.
3. **get** : (be)get (old-fashioned use), be the father of.

PART TWO

The Murder of the King

After the battle King Duncan decided to go on a journey around Scotland. He told Macbeth that he would go and stay in his castle.

'I will be very happy to be your host, sir,' Macbeth told him. 'I will write to my wife so that she can prepare everything for us.'

Macbeth wrote a long letter to his wife. He told her that the King was coming to stay in the castle, and he asked her to prepare everything for the visit. He also told her about the encounter with the three witches, and what they had said about the future.

Lady Macbeth read her husband's letter with great interest and excitement. 'Thane of Cawdor, and then king,' she thought. 'But I know you, husband,' she said to herself. 'You want to be king – but you don't

Macbeth

want to do anything wicked to become king. Your nature is too gentle [1] to be really ambitious. This is a great opportunity for us. Hurry home, my love, and I'll teach you to be cruel for the sake of [2] your ambition. I'll put courage into you!'

When Macbeth and the King arrived at the castle, Lady Macbeth had already made a plan. She told her husband that he had to act very cheerfully and innocently – and that she had made a plan to make him king.

'Leave everything to me,' she said. 'Duncan will never leave the castle alive!'

Macbeth listened to his wife. 'It's true,' he thought, 'I want to be king – but I don't want to kill Duncan – I'm frightened! He's my king, and my guest here in the castle. To murder him would be a terrible crime!'

He argued with Lady Macbeth.

'We cannot kill the King,' he told her. 'He has been a good friend to me, and I can't murder him.'

Lady Macbeth was very angry with her husband.

'Why did you tell me about the three witches?' she demanded angrily. 'They called you "King", didn't they? Be brave, and you can have the throne!' [3]

'But if we fail?' Macbeth asked her. 'What happens to us if we fail?'

'Don't worry about that,' his wife said. 'We won't fail. I have a plan. Duncan's room is guarded by two soldiers. I'll make sure that [4] the soldiers are given a lot of wine tonight,

---

1. **gentle** : mild and calm; not violent.
2. **for the sake of** : in the interests of.
3. **throne** : (here) the position of king.
4. **make sure that** : take action so that.

The Murder of the King

and I'll put something in the wine to make them sleep very heavily. They won't know what's happening. You'll be able to walk past them and into the King's room without anyone seeing you. Then you can kill Duncan, and we'll blame the soldiers [1] for the murder.'

'You're right!' Macbeth said excitedly. 'If the King is killed with the soldiers' knives, everyone will think they're guilty.'

'Exactly,' Lady Macbeth said. 'Who would dare [2] to say that you and I knew anything about it? People might suspect us, but they could never say anything.'

Late that night Macbeth was alone in the castle. He was thinking about the murder, when suddenly he saw a knife in front of him. The knife was red with blood. He was very frightened. When he looked again, the knife had gone.

'It was just my imagination,' he told himself. 'There was nothing there at all.' He shuddered [3] with fear. 'I must be brave,' he told himself. 'If I want to be king, I must be brave.'

He went very quietly to the room of the two soldiers. They were fast asleep, and the room smelt of wine. He took a knife from one of the soldiers, and went into the King's bedroom. The King was asleep. Macbeth killed him with the soldier's knife.

Lady Macbeth saw her husband when he came back out of the soldiers' room.

'Well?' she asked him. 'Did you do it?'

Macbeth was very pale.

'Duncan is dead,' he told her. 'It's a terrible thing I've done. Afterwards,

---

1. **blame the soldiers** : say they are responsible.
2. **dare** : have the courage.
3. **shuddered** : shook, trembled.

Macbeth

I heard a voice. It said; "There will be no more sleep. Macbeth has murdered sleep." It was a frightening voice.'

Lady Macbeth looked at him. Even she was frightened for a moment.

'Did it say anything else?' she asked.

'The voice was very loud,' Macbeth said. 'It cried out, "Macbeth has murdered sleep – Macbeth will never sleep again". I thought everyone in the castle would hear the voice.'

'You're like a child!' Lady Macbeth told him angrily. 'There was no voice, it was only your own fear which you heard. Go and wash the blood from your hands.' Then she noticed the knife in Macbeth's hand.

'But the knife, why are you carrying the knife? You should have left it with the soldiers! Take it back.'

'I can't go back in there,' Macbeth said. 'I'll never go back in there!'

'Give me the knife,' Lady Macbeth ordered. 'I'm not afraid to go in there.'

Lady Macbeth took the knife, and went into the soldiers' room. They were still sleeping. She covered the soldiers with the King's blood, and left the knife in their room. When she came out of the room, she saw that Macbeth was looking at his hands. They were red with blood.

'I'll never be able to wash the blood away,' he said sadly. 'I have done a terrible thing.'

'Look at my hands,' Lady Macbeth told him scornfully. [1] 'They're red like yours – but I'm not afraid like you! A little water will remove the traces [2] of our crime.'

Suddenly they heard a noise at the castle gate. Someone wanted to come in.

'Quickly!' Lady Macbeth commanded. 'We'll go back into our own room – no one must know we've been awake tonight.'

The knocking at the castle gate continued.

---

1. **scornfully** : with contempt.
2. **traces** : signs.

'He saw a knife in front of him. The knife was red with blood.'

Comprehension

1 **Answer the following questions.**

   a. What did King Duncan decide to do after the battle?

   b. What did Macbeth tell his wife in his letter?

   c. Use the words below to describe Macbeth and Lady Macbeth.

gentle   ambitious   brave   cruel   frightened

Macbeth is ....

Lady Macbeth is ....

   d. How does Macbeth first react to his wife's plan to kill the King?

   e. What is Lady Macbeth's plan?

   f. Macbeth sees something before he kills the King. What does he see?

   g. Macbeth hears a voice after he kills the King. What does the voice tell him?

Vocabulary

2 **Match the words in column A with their opposites in column B.**

Column A	Column B
a. large	**1.** asleep
b. cruel	**2.** succeed
c. cheerful	**3.** enemy
d. innocent	**4.** sad
e. host	**5.** tiny
f. friend	**6.** noisy
g. fail	**7.** kind
h. silent	**8.** guilty
i. awake	**9.** guest

3 **Complete these sentences, using the words in the box below.**

> voice   opportunity   blame   crime   knocking

a. Macbeth wants to be king, but he thinks killing Duncan would be a terrible
....

b. Lady Macbeth sees Duncan's visit to the castle as a great .... for her
husband.

c. Lady Macbeth's plan is to .... the soldiers for the murder.

d. When Macbeth hears the ...., he is frightened.

e. After the murder, Macbeth and his wife hear someone .... at the
castle gate.

Grammar

In the text you read:

'Quickly!' Lady Macbeth commanded. 'We'll go back into our own room.'

'Will' is used to indicate the future when the decision to do something is made
at the time of speaking. 'Will' is also used in the following situations:

1   offering to do something

2   agreeing or refusing to do something

3   promising to do something

4   asking someone to do something

4 **Look at the sentences below, and decide which type of 'will' is being used.**

a. I know I was wrong – I'll never do it again!

b. I don't understand this homework. Will you help me with it?

c. My brother's got a new bicycle, but he won't lend it to me.

d. Don't worry, Mrs Jackson. I know you're busy today. I'll collect Sally from
school for you.

e. The phone's ringing – I'll get it.

Listening

 5 After you listen to Part Two of *Macbeth* on the cassette you will hear two short extracts from the original Shakespeare. Listen and answer the following questions.

    a. Which of the extracts comes before the murder, and which comes after the murder?

    b. Listen again and put the first extract into modern English.

Writing

6 Imagine that you are Lady Macbeth. Write a summary of the play so far, from your point of view.

My husband was talking to Banquo after the battle against the Thane of Cawdor when ....

Speaking

7 Consider the following statements about the murder of Duncan. Which statement do you agree with most? Discuss your choice with other people in the class.

    a. The witches are guilty of the murder – without them, the murder would never have happened.

    b. Lady Macbeth is guilty of the murder – she persuaded her husband to do it, and she planned it.

    c. Macbeth is guilty of the murder – he killed Duncan.

Scotland's History

he original inhabitants of Scotland were the Picts and the Scots – the Picts were people of Celtic origin, and the Scots came from Ireland. The Picts and the Scots were fierce [1] warriors, and they defended Scotland against the Romans. In 120 A.D. the Roman Emperor Hadrian built a wall between England and Scotland, to keep the Scottish out. Hadrian's Wall can still be seen today, and is a major tourist attraction.

Scotland was converted to Christianity in the sixth century by missionaries from Ireland. In the ninth century Scotland was united under the same king for the first time, as the country struggled to fight off invasion from the Vikings.

Hadrian's Wall

1. **fierce** : brutal, aggressive.

ra cuuitat parifiata fatib; z latuif cantib; z plau
bz claffiat z laudib; die z notte feqnte feruer z ua
uf omata pannuf tollent cruteabat. fatta z aute

Wallace, Defender of Scotland.

The English king, Edward I, invaded Scotland in the 13th century, and seemed to have defeated the country. In 1314, however, the Scots rebelled against the English, and their leader, Robert Bruce, defeated the English army at the Battle of Bannockburn. After this battle England and Scotland remained separate countries for nearly three hundred years.

Robert Bruce.

Scotland became a Protestant country at the time of the Reformation, although the queen of Scotland, Mary Stuart, was a Roman Catholic. After the death of Elizabeth I of England, Mary Stuart's son, James VI of Scotland, became James I of England. The two countries were thus united for the first time under the same king. The process towards union was brought a step closer in 1707, with the Act of Union – Scotland became part of Great Britain.

Despite the Act of Union the Highland families of Scotland were opposed to English rule in the 1700's. These families were known as 'clans', and each was governed by a 'clan chief'. Each clan wore a distinct tartan by which it could be recognised. The clans rebelled unsuccessfully against the English in 1715 and in 1745. The English treated the rebels with great cruelty, and tried to suppress their

Elizabeth I.

rca ciuitas parisiaca faeib; ȝ latinis cantib; ȝ plau
bȝ classieis ȝ laudib; die ȝ nocte seȝnit serici ȝ ua
ús oznata pannis tollent eruitabat. facta ȝ ante

traditional way of life. The wearing of tartans was forbidden, as was the use of
Gaelic, the traditional language.

Towards the end of the 1700's the clan chiefs realised that they could become
wealthy by turning their attention to the wool trade. They began investing in
sheep, and they forced their own people to leave their Highland farms. This
became known as the 'Highland clearances'. The clan chiefs destroyed the old
Highland way of life, and many Highland Scots left the country to settle in
America, Australia and Canada.

During the 20th century the Scottish economy received a welcome boost [1] from
the development of off-shore oil-fields, [2] and there was a revival of interest in
Scottish independence. A referendum for Scottish devolution was narrowly

1. **boost** : help, advancement.
2. **off-shore oil-fields** : areas under the seabed where there is oil.

defeated in the 1970's, and the present Labour government has plans to give the country its own parliament, or Scottish Assembly.

Today Scotland has an important tourist industry. Many 'Scottish Americans', the descendants of Highlanders who left Scotland during the Highland clearances of the past, come to explore their past. It is also a popular holiday destination for the Japanese, who come to visit Scotland's celebrated golf courses, and sample its famous whiskies.

1 **Where did the Scots originally come from?**

    a. Wales

    b. England

    c. Germany

    d. Ireland

2 **What was the effect of the Act of Union?**

    a. James VI of Scotland became James I of England.

    b. Scotland became a Protestant country.

    c. Scotland became a part of Great Britain.

    d. Scotland defeated the English and became independent.

3 **How did the clan chiefs destroy the old Highland way of life?**

4 **Scottish history has been characterised by many battles and rebellions. Write a passage about the most important of these. Use the information in the section above to help you.**

PART THREE

Macbeth, King of Scotland

The knocking on the castle gate was now very loud. The porter was very slow to open the gate.

'All right, all right, I can hear you,' he called out angrily. 'Don't be in such a hurry!'

Two of the King's men, Macduff and Lennox, entered the castle. Macduff was annoyed with the porter because he had been slow to open the gate. He looked at him angrily.

'Did you go to bed late, my friend?' he asked. 'Perhaps you drank too much before you went to bed – is that why you were so slow to open the gate?'

'You're right, sir,' the porter admitted. 'I did drink too much before I went to bed.'

'I see we have woken Macbeth with our noise,' said Macduff. 'Good morning to you,' he said politely. 'Is the King awake yet?'

Macbeth

'He's still sleeping,' Macbeth said. 'Shall I wake him for you?'

'It's all right,' said Macduff. 'I'll wake him myself. He asked me to come early this morning.'

Macduff went off to wake the King, and Lennox and Macbeth stayed near the castle gate, talking.

'What a strange night it's been!' Lennox said to Macbeth. 'The wind blew fiercely [1] all night. The chimneys [2] in our house were blown down. Some people said they could hear horrible screams.'

'It was just bad weather,' Macbeth told him. 'It didn't mean anything.'

After a few minutes they heard a shout from the King's room. Macduff was shouting.

'Help! Help!'

'What is it? What's the matter?' cried Lennox. 'Is it the King?'

Macduff came out of the King's room. He was very pale. 'It's dreadful,' [3] he cried, 'too dreadful! Go and look for yourselves.'

'Come on,' said Macbeth, and he rushed with Lennox up to the King's room.

'Murder!' shouted Macduff. 'There's a traitor [4] in the castle. Sound the alarm!'

People began to wake, and to come out of their rooms.

'What is it?' asked Lady Macbeth, 'Why is there such a noise?'

Macduff approached King Duncan's two sons.

'I have terrible news for you,' he told them.

'Tell us,' said Malcolm. 'Is it the King?' He looked at his brother, Donalblain.

1. **fiercely** : very strongly.
2. **chimneys** : pipes through which smoke goes up into the air through the roof of a building.
3. **dreadful** : terrible.
4. **traitor** : someone who is an enemy of his own country.

'Macduff came out of the King's room.
He was very pale. "It's dreadful," he cried, "too dreadful!"'

Macbeth

'Yes, tell us,' said Donalblain. 'What about our father?'

Macduff looked very serious.

'I found him,' he said. 'He's been murdered!'

Macbeth and Lennox now came down from the King's room. They joined the shocked and frightened crowd of people.

'It's true,' Macbeth announced, 'Duncan has been murdered.'

'But who – !' cried Malcolm and Donalblain. 'Who would kill the King?'

'It was the two soldiers,' Lennox announced. 'When we went up there just now, we found them. They were sleeping very heavily, and they were covered with the King's blood. When we asked them questions, they looked amazed, and couldn't say anything. It was obviously them who killed the King.'

'Why did they do it?' asked Macduff. 'We must find out why they did it!'

'We'll never know,' Macbeth said. 'I killed them straight away! I wish I hadn't been so angry.'

There was silence. Everyone looked at Macbeth for a moment.

Then Macduff spoke.

'Now we'll never know why they did it, or if someone paid them to do the murder.'

'I'm sorry,' said Macbeth. 'But when I saw them covered in the King's blood, and when I smelt the wine on their breath, [1] I was angry – I loved the King!'

'Oh, the King, the poor King!' cried Lady Macbeth. She looked wildly [2] at everybody. 'What a terrible thing to happen here, in our house. Who could have done it?' Then she fell to the floor.

---

1. **breath** [breθ] : air that comes out of your mouth.
2. **wildly** : in great excitement.

Macbeth, King of Scotland

'She's fainted,[1] the shock is too great,' Macduff said. 'Someone help her.'

Macbeth stepped forward. He picked up his wife, and carried her away. Banquo now spoke for the first time.

'We need to plan what to do,' he said. 'I suggest we all go back to our rooms. We'll return here in one hour. Then we can decide what is to be done.'

Everyone agreed with Banquo's suggestion, and they agreed to meet in one hour.

As they were walking back to their room in the castle, Duncan's two sons spoke quietly to each other. They were shocked and frightened by their father's murder.

'Listen to me,' Donalblain said to his brother. 'I don't feel safe here. Someone has killed our father, and I don't believe Macbeth's story about the two soldiers.'

'I don't, either,' Malcolm told him. 'Why would the soldiers murder our father like that? Why would they drink wine afterwards? We'll never know what really happened now that the soldiers are dead.'

'If you want my opinion,' Donalblain said, 'Macbeth was too quick to kill them.'

Malcolm looked at him strangely. 'What do you mean?' he asked. 'What are you trying to say?'

'Just this,' said Donalblain. 'I don't think Macbeth killed them because he was angry. I think he killed them because he didn't want us to ask them what happened. I think – '

'You suspect Macbeth of the murder?' his brother asked. 'You think he killed our father? But why would he do that?'

'I don't know,' Donalblain said. 'I think we should get away from this castle before anything happens to us. Whoever killed our father may still

---

1. **fainted** : lost consciousness.

Macbeth

be here – and we may be the next to die! Let's leave Scotland, shall we?'

'I agree,' Malcolm said. 'Let's go away from here. I'll go to England. I've got friends there, and they'll help me.'

'And I'll go to Ireland,' Donalblain said. 'I'll feel safer if I'm a long way from Scotland.'

Malcolm and Donalblain left Macbeth's castle very quietly. They did not tell anyone they were going.

The others were surprised that Duncan's two sons had left the castle secretly. Suspicion fell on Donalblain and Malcolm. Macduff was the first to say what they were all beginning to think.

'It must have been Donalblain and Malcolm,' he told the others. 'I think I know what happened,' he said. 'Malcolm and Donalblain paid the two soldiers to kill Duncan because they wanted the throne for themselves. We must make sure that they suffer for this terrible crime!'

Everyone agreed with Macduff.

'Donalblain and Malcolm are murderers,' they said.

'Who will we have as our new king?' asked Macduff. 'We don't want Donalblain or Malcolm. Let's choose someone who was loyal to Duncan.'

'Let's make Macbeth the new king!' the thanes decided. 'He deserves to be king – he was Duncan's loyal friend. Remember how brave he was in the battle against the rebels and the King of Norway.'

The thanes of Scotland made Macbeth the new King of Scotland.

Comprehension

1 **Arrange the events below in the correct order.**

    a. Macbeth kills the two soldiers.

    b. Macduff and Lennox enter the castle.

    c. Macduff finds the King dead.

    d. Malcolm and Donalblain decide to leave the castle.

    e. Macduff suspects Malcolm and Donalblain of the murder.

    f. Macbeth and Lennox go into the King's room.

    g. Macduff is angry with the porter.

    h. Lady Macbeth falls to the floor.

2 **Why does Macbeth really go to the King's room with Lennox?**

    a. To see if the King is dead.

    b. To kill the two soldiers.

    c. To catch the murderers.

3 **Why do Malcolm and Donalblain leave the castle secretly?**

Vocabulary

4 **Match the words with their opposites from the text.**

    a. soft   ....

    b. fast   ....

    c. late   ....

    d. pleasant   ....

    e. false   ....

    f. noisily   ....

Grammar

Question tags

Question tags are put onto the ends of sentences, either to make a question or to provide emphasis.

She's Italian, isn't she?
You can drive, can't you?
They went to America, didn't they?
You're not going to have another ice-cream, are you?
Be quiet, won't you?
Don't spend a lot today, will you?

In the text you read:

'Whoever killed our father may still be here – and we may be the next to die! Let's leave Scotland, **shall we**?'

5 **Complete the following sentences with an appropriate question tag.**

    a. He's been late for work every day this week, ...?

    b. You haven't done your home-work, ...?

    c. Let's go to the cinema this evening, ...?

    d. You can speak French, ...

    e. They came home very late last night, ...?

Must

The modal auxiliary verb 'must' is used to indicate self-imposed obligation:
*I **must** make a living for my family.*

It is also used to indicate an order:
*You **must** be in bed at midnight.*

It is also used to indicate logical deduction:
*The lights are on. They **must** still be awake.*

In the text you read:

'It **must have been** Malcolm and Donalblain.'
What does 'must' express here?

6 Write three sentences using 'must' to express:

- obligation ....
- order ....
- logical deduction ....

Listening

 7 After you listen to Part Three of *Macbeth* on the cassette you will hear more of the conversation between Malcolm and Donalblain. Listen and answer the following questions.

a. What is Malcolm going to ask the English king?

b. What do people say about the English king?

c. What does Donalblain ask his brother to do?

Writing

8 Imagine you are one of the two soldiers who were guarding the King and that you managed to escape. Describe what happened that evening.

Speaking

9 Do you think Malcolm and Donalblain have done the right thing to run away from the castle?

PART FOUR

Banquo's Ghost

Banquo was unhappy when he remembered what the witches had promised Macbeth.

'They said you would be Thane of Cawdor, and then King of Scotland. Everything they said has come true. Now you are the king. Perhaps it was you who killed Duncan, and not Donalblain and Malcolm!' He did not like to think that Macbeth was a murderer. 'And what was it that they promised me?' he said to himself. "Less than Macbeth, but more than Macbeth", was that it? No, there was something else. Let me see if I can remember. Ah, yes, that was it. "You will never be king, but your children's children will be kings." I wonder what that means, and whether it will come true as well?'

Macbeth was also thinking about what the witches had said.

'They said I would be Thane of Cawdor, and then King of Scotland. Everything they said has come true. But there was something else, something about Banquo. Ah, yes, they told Banquo that his "children's children will be kings". Have I killed Duncan for nothing – will Banquo's

Banquo's Ghost

son Fleance get the crown after me?' Macbeth thought about his old friend. 'Banquo's dangerous!' he said to himself. 'He knows about the witches – perhaps he suspects that it was me who killed Duncan. I'm afraid of him.'

Every day Macbeth's fear of Banquo and his son increased. 'I must do something,' he told himself. 'I can't live in fear all my life.' Then he thought of a wicked plan.

One day Macbeth invited all the thanes to a feast at the palace.

'Make sure that you come, my old friend,' he said to Banquo. 'The feast is in your honour.'

'I will be there,' said Banquo.

'And bring Fleance with you,' said Macbeth. 'The feast is for him as well.'

'We will be there,' said Banquo. 'We are riding out this afternoon, but we will be back at the castle for the feast.'

'Tomorrow we must have a long talk,' Macbeth went on. 'I hear that Malcolm and Donalblain have gone to England and Ireland. They are trying to make trouble for me, and we have to decide what to do about them.'

'Very well,' Banquo replied. 'Tomorrow we'll talk about that problem.'

Macbeth smiled grimly 1 to himself. 'There will be no feast for you tonight, my friend,' he thought. 'And no talk tomorrow. Tonight you and Fleance will both be dead. My men will kill you both when you are out riding. With you and Fleance dead, I will be safe.'

Lady Macbeth knew nothing of Macbeth's plan to kill Banquo and Fleance. She only knew that Macbeth was worried about something. He had been unhappy since the murder of Duncan, and was sleeping badly.

'You must forget about the murder,' she told him. 'The past is the past – we can't change it now.'

'We must be safe from danger,' Macbeth answered. 'It's true that Duncan is dead, and I am king. But still – '

---

1. **grimly** : seriously.

Macbeth

'Try to be more cheerful,' Lady Macbeth said. 'Remember there is the feast tonight.'

'I'll be cheerful, tonight, my love,' Macbeth promised her. 'And yet I keep thinking about Banquo and Fleance. They worry me.'

'What can we do about them?' asked his wife.

'I have already done something,' Macbeth told her. 'It's better that you don't know about it.'

Late that evening, three men were hiding near the palace.

'Are you sure Banquo and Fleance will come this way?' said one of the men.

'They'll come this way,' answered another.

'And when they do, we'll kill them both,' said the third man. 'Macbeth wants them both to die.'

'Here they are!' said the first man. 'I can hear the horses.'

The three men stood up, with their knives in their hands. They could see Banquo and Fleance in front of them.

'Now!' cried the third man, as he pulled Banquo off his horse. He put the knife to Banquo's heart.

'Attack!' cried the other two men. They approached Fleance.

'Ride, Fleance, ride!' shouted Banquo. 'It's a trap.'

Fleance rode away as fast as he could.

Macbeth welcomed the thanes when they arrived at the castle for the feast.

'I'm happy to see you all,' he said. He walked around the table, shaking their hands and smiling. 'Tonight we will enjoy ourselves with food and wine,' he said.

As Macbeth was walking around the table talking to his guests, he saw one of the murderers enter the room. He went up to him.

'Well?' he asked quietly. 'How did it go?'

'Banquo is dead,' the man replied.

'And Fleance?' asked Macbeth. 'Tell me that Fleance is dead as well!'

Banquo's Ghost

'Fleance escaped us,' the man said. 'He is free.'

'Then I'm not safe, after all. Fleance is dangerous,' Macbeth whispered. He looked at the murderer. 'You'd better go,' he ordered. 'There is blood on your face. We'll talk more tomorrow.' He sighed, and looked worried.

Lady Macbeth was looking at her husband. She knew that something was wrong.

'Tonight is a feast,' she called to him. 'The King must be cheerful tonight.'

'You're right, my love,' Macbeth told her. 'Tonight we will eat and be happy with our guests.'

'Will Your Majesty sit with us?' Lennox asked politely.

'Where shall I sit?' asked Macbeth. 'All the chairs are taken.'

'Here, Your Majesty, sit here,' said Lennox. 'There is an empty chair beside me.'

Macbeth looked at the chair beside Lennox – he saw the ghost of Banquo sitting there! Suddenly he began to tremble, [1] and he went [2] very pale.

'I didn't do it!' he cried out to the ghost. 'Don't sit there looking at me like that. I didn't do it!'

The ghost of Banquo looked steadily [3] at Macbeth for a moment.

'What's the matter with the King?' the thanes said. 'Why is he so frightened, and who is he talking to – that chair's empty!'

'It's just an illness of his,' said Lady Macbeth. 'He's like this sometimes. He'll be all right in a moment.'

She went up to her husband.

'What's the matter with you?' she whispered angrily. 'Remember your guests. Where's your courage?'

'My courage!' responded Macbeth. 'I'm a brave man to look at that ghost and not run away.'

---

1. **tremble** : shake with fear.
2. **went** : (here) became.
3. **steadily** : persistently, without interruption.

Macbeth

Lady Macbeth was angry now.

'What ghost? There's nothing there,' she told him. 'The ghost you see is like the knife you saw before you killed Duncan – it's just your fear and your imagination. There's nothing there.'

'But look at it!' her husband whispered. 'It's Banquo, can't you see?'

As Macbeth spoke, the ghost of Banquo disappeared from his sight.

'I tell you it was Banquo,' Macbeth whispered to his wife. 'I saw him there!'

Banquo's Ghost

'I tell you there was nothing there,' his wife whispered.

'How is it possible?' he was thinking. 'There have been terrible crimes in the past – but dead men never came back to torment their killers before!'

'Remember your guests,' Lady Macbeth warned him.

Macbeth turned to the thanes.

Macbeth

'Forgive me,' he said. 'It is an illness of mine. Let's eat and drink, my friends.' He took up a glass, and filled it with wine. Then he raised the glass. 'To all of us!' he cried. 'To us, and to Banquo – I wish Banquo could be here with us tonight.'

The thanes raised their glasses high in the air.

'To us and Banquo!' they cried.

At that moment Banquo's ghost came back into the room, and looked again at Macbeth.

Macbeth stared at the ghost. He was frightened.

'Why look at me?' he shouted. Now he was angry with the ghost. 'Away with you – there's nothing for you here!' He looked at his wife. 'How can you look at him, and not be afraid?' he asked. 'I am a brave man, but he frightens me.'

'What does the King mean? What is he looking at?' asked the thanes. 'What's the matter with the King?'

'It's nothing,' replied Lady Macbeth. 'It's just the King's illness. It will pass. But for now, let's part – the King needs to rest because he is ill.'

The thanes left the table. Macbeth and his wife talked together.

'Macduff didn't come tonight,' Macbeth said. 'Why do you think he didn't come?'

'I don't know,' his wife replied.

'I don't trust any of them,' Macbeth said to his wife. 'Not a single one of them. They are all my enemies. I'll go back to the three witches,' Macbeth decided. 'I must find out from them what is going to happen. Even if they tell me the worst, I must know!'

'You're tired,' Lady Macbeth told him. 'You need to sleep.'

Comprehension

1 **Answer the following questions.**

    a. Why is Banquo unhappy?

    b. Why does Macbeth want to kill Banquo and Fleance?

    c. Why does Macbeth tell the murderer that Fleance is 'dangerous'?

    d. *'I didn't do it!' he cried out to the ghost. 'Don't sit there looking at me like that. I didn't do it!'*

        What does Macbeth mean by these words to Banquo's ghost?

    e. Why does Lady Macbeth tell the Thanes that Macbeth is ill?

Vocabulary

2 **Give a definition of the following words using a monolingual dictionary if necessary.**

MURDER ....

....

GHOST ....

....

FEAST ....

....

3 **Fill in the gaps with words from the text.**

    a. The .... had promised that Macbeth would become king.

    b. Macbeth did not want Fleance to have the .... after him.

    c. Macbeth .... the guests when they arrived at the feast.

    d. Lady Macbeth did not see Banquo's ....

Grammar

What tense is used to indicate that one action happened before another? Look at the sentence below and the tenses used.

Banquo **was** unhappy when he **remembered** what the witches **had promised** Macbeth.

4 **Put the verbs in brackets into the correct tense.**

a. I .... *(find)* the literature course easy because I .... *(read)* all the books during the holidays.

b. She .... *(be)* late for work this morning, because she .... *(lose)* the car keys.

c. He .... *(eat)* a big lunch, so he .... *(not want)* a large dinner.

d. He .... (save) a lot of money before he .... *(give up)* work.

Listening

5 **After you listen to Part Four of *Macbeth* on the cassette you will hear a conversation between two of the thanes who were at the feast. Before you listen, try and fill in the gaps with the words from the box. Then listen and check your answers.**

agree	Macduff	strange	think	arguing	do
like	mad	hello	cheerful	suspects	learned

First Thane: What did you .... of the feast the other night?

Second Thane: It was all right at first, wasn't it? Macbeth said .... to everybody, and he seemed .... and happy.

First Thane: Then he was ...., wasn't he? Who was he ....
with? What did he mean when he said 'I didn't .... it'? I think the Queen
is right. Macbeth is .... sometimes!

Second Thane: I don't .... I don't think Macbeth is mad, exactly. It's
funny [1] how he mentioned Banquo – and now we've .... that Banquo is
dead. I don't .... it at all.

First Thane: You're not the only one who doesn't like it. .... wasn't at
the feast, did you notice that? I think he .... Macbeth of something. A lot of
people don't trust the King now.

Writing

6 Imagine that you are one of the servants in Macbeth's castle. Write a letter to a
friend describing the King's behaviour at the feast.

Speaking

7 Do you think Macbeth is mad, or do you think there is another explanation for his
strange behaviour? Consider the following facts:

- The dagger which Macbeth saw before he killed Duncan
- The voice which he heard after he killed Duncan
- The blood on his hands after he killed Duncan
- The ghost of Banquo which he saw at the feast

---

1. **funny** : strange.

𝔚𝔦𝔱𝔠𝔥𝔠𝔯𝔞𝔣𝔱 𝔦𝔫 𝔖𝔥𝔞𝔨𝔢𝔰𝔭𝔢𝔞𝔯𝔢'𝔰 𝔗𝔦𝔪𝔢

Many of Shakespeare's plays contain supernatural elements that are difficult for modern audiences to accept. In *Julius Caesar*, for example, there are many strange portents and omens [1] before the assassination of Caesar. In *A Midsummer Night's Dream* there are fairies. In *Hamlet* the action of the play depends on the appearance of the ghost of Hamlet's father. In *Macbeth* there are the witches and Banquo's ghost.

Poster for Harley Granville Barker's production of A Midsummer Night's Dream, *1914*

It is impossible for us to know what Shakespeare himself believed about ghosts and other supernatural phenomena. Quite a lot is known, however, about what other people believed in Shakespeare's time. Belief in witches was widespread in Shakespeare's time. It was said that witches were given their power by the devil, and that they could be very dangerous. Many women were executed because they were said to be witches.

At around the time that *Macbeth* was written there was a very public debate about witches in England. Scot, in his *Discovery of Witchcraft,* (1584),

---

1. **portents and omens** : indications of what is likely to happen in the future.

argued that witches did not really exist. He said that the women accused of being witches were often the victims of false accusation. King James took a personal interest in the subject of witchcraft, and wrote a book on the subject, *Demonology* (1597). The King believed that witches existed, and secretly attended the trials of women accused of being witches. He made sure that the law against them was strengthened.

In the theatre, witchcraft and the devil were popular themes with audiences. Miracle plays had been popular from the 14th century until the 16th century. These frequently had roles for devils and supernatural characters. Although the miracle plays had died out by the time *Macbeth* was written, fascination with supernatural themes was still popular.

Hamlet sees the ghost of his father.

One of Shakespeare's contemporaries, Christopher Marlowe, wrote a very popular play about possession by the Devil, called *The Tragical History of Dr Faustus,* (1604).

A lot of the people who went to see Shakespeare's plays would have found the witches' presence in *Macbeth* exciting and frightening.

1 Match the supernatural elements with the play in which they appear.

SUPERNATURAL EVENTS	PLAY
a. Strange portents and omens	**1.** Hamlet
b. Fairies	**2.** Macbeth
c. Ghost	**3.** A Midsummer Night's Dream
d. Witches	**4.** Julius Caesar

2 Two books about witchcraft are mentioned in the text. What are their titles, and who wrote them?

3 Which of Shakespeare's contemporaries wrote a play about possession by the Devil?

4 What was the attitude of King James I to witchcraft?

5 According to the Oxford Advanced Learner's Dictionary, miracle plays were a form of Medieval drama based on events in the Bible or the lives of saints. What can you add to this information, from what you have read in this section? How did miracle plays influence the theatre over the centuries?

6 How did audiences in Shakespeare's time react to portrayals of the supernatural? What is your own view of such phenomena as ghosts and witches?

PART FIVE

Macbeth and the Spirits

That night the witches were in their usual place where they were soon joined by the Goddess, Hecate. She was angry with them because they had spoken to Macbeth.

'You've been playing with Macbeth!' she screamed at them. 'You've been making promises to him – and he believes you. Who gave you permission to do that? Why did you do it without asking me first? You were wrong to do anything without asking me first!'

The witches were afraid of Hecate because she was very powerful.

'Listen to me,' Hecate said. 'Macbeth will come to you in the morning. He wants to know his future. This time you must do as I tell you.'

Macbeth went out in the morning to meet the three witches. When he found them they were standing over their cooking-pot. One of the witches

threw a toad ¹ into the pot, and they all laughed.

'A toad, yes, a toad!' the others cried. 'That's good, a toad! We'll put that in.'

Then they began to sing as they stirred the contents of the pot:

"Round, around, around, about, about,
Wicked staying in, good staying out.
By the feeling in my thumb
Something wicked is about to come."

Macbeth looked at the witches with disgust.

'What are you doing?' he asked. 'What kind of magic is this?'

'We can't tell you,' one of the witches replied.

'I have come here,' Macbeth told them, 'to ask you something. You must tell me the truth!'

'Ask us your question,' the first witch said.

'We will answer,' the second witch said.

'If you don't trust ² us,' the third witch said, 'our masters will come to answer your question. Would you prefer that?'

'Call your masters,' commanded Macbeth. 'I want to see them. Call them for me now.'

The witches stirred their cooking-pot, and spoke some magic words. Suddenly Macbeth saw a head floating in the air in front of him. Macbeth began to speak.

'Tell me, whoever you are – '

'Don't speak!' the witches shouted. 'Listen, but don't speak. He knows what you want.'

The head began to speak:

1. **toad** :
2. **trust** : believe.

Macbeth and the Spirits

'Macbeth, be careful of Macduff!
That is my message – it's enough.'

Then the head disappeared. The witches spoke some
more magic words, and a second spirit came. The second
spirit had this message for Macbeth:

'Macbeth, be brave and laugh to scorn [1]
The power of man. No man of woman
born
Can hurt Macbeth.'

The second spirit disappeared. The witches spoke
their magic words again, and a third
spirit appeared. The third spirit
said:

'Macbeth will never be defeated
until Birnam Wood comes to
Dunsinane Hill and fights against
him.'

Macbeth considered the three
messages of the spirits.
'They say that I should be careful of Macduff,'
he thought. 'But Macduff is a man, and they say that
no man born of woman can hurt me, so that must
mean that Macduff can't hurt me! They say I can't be
defeated until Birnam Wood comes to Dunsinane Hill

1. **scorn** : despise.

to fight me. No one can command a wood to fight, so that must mean that I will never be defeated! These messages give me courage.'

'You have done well,' he told the witches, 'and I am happy with what you have told me. But there is one other thing I want to know. You told Banquo that his children's children would be kings – is that really true?'

When they heard this question, all the witches shouted,

'Ask no more! Ask no more!'

Macbeth became angry.

'I must have an answer!' he shouted. 'Tell me the truth – will Banquo's family be kings after me?'

The witches stopped dancing. Then they sang together:

'Show the future, break his heart,
Then we witches will depart.'

Macbeth looked, and out of the cooking-pot he saw a figure appear – it was Banquo! Then he saw a line of kings standing next to Banquo. All of the kings had the same face, and they all looked at Macbeth. Banquo smiled at Macbeth, and then he pointed at the kings. Slowly the image disappeared.

Macbeth put his head in his hands. He was in despair [1] now. So it was true what the witches had said before, that Banquo's family would be the future Kings of Scotland!

'All my crimes for nothing!' he thought. 'Banquo's family will be kings after me, and no one will remember Macbeth!'

1. **in despair** : desperate, miserable.

'Out of the cooking-pot he saw a figure appear – it was Banquo!'

Comprehension

1 **The witches tell Macbeth not to speak to the spirits because:**

   a. human beings cannot speak directly to spirits.

   b. it is dangerous to speak to spirits directly.

   c. they already know his thoughts.

   d. Macbeth is not important enough to speak to spirits.

   e. they would not answer him.

2 **Macbeth receives four messages from the spirits. Two of the messages make him happy, and two of them make him unhappy. Which are they?**

Messages which make Macbeth happy	Messages which make Macbeth unhappy

3 **'All my crimes for nothing!' What does Macbeth mean by this?**

Vocabulary

4 The words on the left come from the text. Use a dictionary to match them with their synonyms on the right.

a. scream	**1.** repugnance
b. permission	**2.** chief
c. wicked	**3.** charm
d. disgust	**4.** damage
e. magic	**5.** authorisation
f. master	**6.** evil
g. hurt	**7.** screech

Grammar

5 Put the conversation between Macbeth and the witches into reported speech.

e.g.: 'What are you doing?' he asked. 'What kind of magic is this?'

He asked them what they were doing and what kind of magic it was.

a. 'We can't tell you,' one of the witches replied.

....

b. 'I have come here,' Macbeth told them, 'to ask you something. You must tell me the truth!'

....

c. 'Ask us your question,' the first witch said to Macbeth.

....

d. 'We will answer,' the second witch said.

....

e. 'If you don't trust us,' the third witch said, 'our masters will come to answer your question. Would you prefer that?'

....

f. 'Call your masters,' commanded Macbeth. 'I want to see them.'

....

Listening

 6 After you listen to Part Five of *Macbeth* on the cassette you will hear a conversation between a teacher and students. Listen carefully, and then answer the questions which follow.

    a. What does Jenny think of the first message?

    b. Why does Richard disagree with Jenny about the first message?

    c. What does Jenny think of the third message?

    d. What does Richard think of the fourth message?

Writing

7 What do you think happens next in the story?

Speaking

8 Look at the messages from the spirits again. What do *you* think they mean?

PART SIX

Macduff

Some of the thanes of Scotland began to be suspicious of Macbeth after Banquo was murdered. They began to think that Macbeth had been involved in the death of his friend.

'I don't think Malcolm and Donalblain paid the two soldiers to kill Duncan,' one of them said. 'They wouldn't have killed their father, because they loved him too much.'

'Why do you think they ran away then?' asked another thane.

'I think they ran away because they were frightened,' the first thane said. 'Perhaps they were frightened that someone would kill them as well.'

'What about the soldiers?' asked another thane. 'Do you really think it was them who killed the King?'

Macduff spoke next.

'I'll tell you what I think,' he said. 'I think the man who murdered Duncan wanted to become king himself,' he said. 'I think Macbeth did it.'

'And Banquo?' asked another thane. 'Who killed Banquo, I wonder? Banquo and Macbeth were good friends, weren't they?'

'I don't know about that,' Macduff said. 'But I don't feel safe here in

Macbeth

Scotland – I'm going to England to ask the English king for help. Something is very wrong in Scotland. We live in bad times.'

Macbeth knew that the thanes were turning against him. One by one his friends abandoned him, and he felt lonely and afraid.

'I will kill all my enemies!' he decided. He thought about Macduff. 'I don't trust him,' he said to himself. 'The spirit said that Macduff was dangerous. Macduff's family will be the first to die.'

Macbeth sent some of his men to Macduff's castle.

Macduff

Macduff was now in England, but Macbeth's men found Lady Macduff and her children in the castle.

'Where is your husband?' one of the men asked Lady Macduff.

'He's not here,' Lady Macduff said. 'He's gone, and you'll never find him.'

'Macduff's a traitor!' the man cried.

'You're a liar,'[1] said the little boy. 'My father's not a traitor!'

The man took out his sword, and killed Lady Macduff and her son.

1. **liar** : someone who doesn't tell the truth.

Macbeth

Macduff was in England at the court of the English king. Here he met Duncan's son, Malcolm. Malcolm wanted the English king to send an army into Scotland against Macbeth, and he told Macduff about the plan.

'Will you fight with us?' he asked. 'We need a man like you with the army.'

'I don't know,' Macduff said. 'It's true that Macbeth is a bad man, and a bad king – but to take an army into Scotland would be wrong. Give me time to think what I should do.'

As they were talking, Ross joined them. He had just arrived from Scotland. Malcolm was pleased to see his friend.

'What's the news from Scotland?' he asked.

'All the news is bad,' replied Ross. 'There is talk of a rebellion against Macbeth. Scotland is in danger. We need you back in Scotland, Macduff. '

'And my family?' asked Macduff. 'Is my family all right?'

'This is the worst news of all,' Ross told him. 'Macbeth's men went to your castle, and they killed your wife.'

'What about my children?' asked Macduff. 'Are my children safe?'

Ross looked very serious.

'They killed everybody,' he said. 'Your wife, your children, even the servants in the castle.'

'My children!' cried Macduff. 'My little children dead!'

'Now will you join us?' asked Malcolm. 'We're going to take an army into Scotland. Seyward will command the soldiers. We'll attack Macbeth. Think of the people he has killed – my father Duncan, Banquo, and now your family. Let's defeat [1] him!'

'All right,' said Macduff. 'I'll come with you, but I want to be the one who kills Macbeth. I want revenge [2] for what he did to my wife and children!'

1. **defeat** : fight against and win a victory.
2. **revenge** : punishment for a bad action.

Comprehension

1 One of the thanes says that he does not think Malcolm and Donalblain killed Duncan. What reason does he give for his opinion? Choose from one of the options below.

    a. They were too frightened to kill the King.

    b. The two soldiers killed the King.

    c. Macbeth killed the King.

    d. They loved their father.

    e. They ran away before the King was killed.

2 Macduff thinks he knows who killed Duncan, and why. Choose from one of the options below.

    a. The soldiers killed him, because they were paid by Malcolm and Donalblain.

    b. Malcolm and Donalblain killed him, because they were frightened of him.

    c. Macbeth killed him, because he wanted to become king.

    d. Lady Macbeth killed him, because she wanted to help her husband.

    e. Banquo killed him, because he wanted to become king.

3 How does Macduff react when Malcolm first asks him to fight with the army? Choose from one of the options below.

    a. He agrees to fight because he wants to defeat Macbeth.

    b. He says that it would be wrong to fight against the King.

    c. He agrees to fight because Macbeth is a bad man, and a bad king.

    d. He refuses to fight because he does not like Malcolm.

    e. He agrees to fight because Macbeth has killed his family.

Vocabulary

4 The English language has many words which derive from Latin, as well as many words with an Anglo-Saxon origin. Use a dictionary to find the origins of the following words.

	Origin	Original Word
feast		
party		
murder		
assassin		
fight		
king		

Grammar

Phrasal verbs

In the text you read:

a. 'Why do you think they **ran away**, then?'

b. Macbeth knew that the thanes were **turning against** him.

In these sentences the basic meaning of the verb is changed.

'to run away' means to avoid a danger or difficulty

'to turn against' means to become an enemy

5 Find and underline the phrasal verbs in the sentences below and then match the meanings of the phrasal verbs with the correct definition on the following page.

a. I was walking in town when I ran into an old friend of mine. I hadn't seen him for years, and I was very surprised to see him again.

b. There isn't any coffee in the house. When did we run out of it?

c. We went to see a magic show last night. My son was delighted when the magician's cat turned into a bird and flew away!

d. The film started badly, but it turned out all right and we enjoyed it.

   1. to become   **2.** to meet someone by chance

   3. to use the last of something   **4.** to finish

Listening

 6 After you listen to Part Six of *Macbeth* on the cassette you will hear a short extract from the original Shakespeare. Before you listen, try to fill in the gaps with words from the box. Then listen carefully and check your answers.

> all   comforted   children   revenge   servants

Macduff: My .... too?

Ross: Wife, children, ..., all

    That could be found.

Macduff: And I must be from thence! [1]

    My wife killed too?

Ross: I have said.

Malcolm: Be ....

    Let's make us medicines of our great ....

    To cure this deadly grief. [2]

Macduff: He has no children.

    All my pretty ones? Did you say ....?

    O hell-kite! [3] All? What, all my pretty chickens

    And their dam [4] at one fell swoop? [5]

   1. **And I must be from thence** : And I had to be away at the time!
   2. **grief** : sadness.
   3. **hell-kite** : bird from hell.
   4. **dam** : mother.
   5. **one fell swoop** : in one action.

Writing

7 'There is enough for the needy, but not for the greedy.' Comment on this statement.

....
....
....
....
....
....
....
....

Speaking

8 Macduff wants revenge for the murder of his family. What are your feelings about revenge? Can revenge ever be a good thing?

....
....
....
....
....
....
....
....

The Wonders of Scotland

The scenery of Scotland varies greatly from rich green fields to bleak mountains. The country is usually cool and there is generous rainfall throughout the year, particularly in the west. The Highlands of Scotland are in the north, and the Lowlands in the south. The highest mountains are the Grampians in the central Highlands, and Ben Nevis is the highest peak. Scotland is famous for its many beautiful castles. Some of these are still in use, and others are romantic ruins which evoke the drama and excitement of Scotland's past.

Loch Lochy.

Cawdor Castle

Cawdor Castle, which now belongs to the Earls of Cawdor, used to belong to the Thanes of Cawdor. According to legend, it was here that Macbeth murdered King Duncan.
The castle is a popular place for tourists to visit.

Edinburgh Castle

Edinburgh castle is one of the most beautiful castles in Britain, and is visited by many tourists every year. The oldest part of the castle was built in 1130.

Balmoral Castle

Balmoral Castle was bought by Queen Victoria and her husband in 1845. Since then it has been a favourite residence for the Royal family, who usually spend their summer holidays there.

Glamis Castle

Glamis Castle was the childhood home of Elizabeth, the Queen Mother. According to legend some of the scenes in Shakespeare's *Macbeth* were set here. The castle is said to contain many ghosts, and there is a mysterious locked crypt in the foundations of the building.

Part of the fascination of Scotland comes from the romantic atmosphere of its traditions and folklore. Bagpipes and tartans were originally connected with the clan system of the Highland way of life. There has been a revival

of interest in Scottish folklore in recent years, and it is possible to visit folkclubs to hear the old Border Ballads sung and recited, as well as the popular songs of the national poet, Robert Burns. Edinburgh plays host to two important events every year. First there is the Tattoo in front of the castle. The bagpipe and drum bands from Scotland march in a parade, playing their own music. The Tattoo ends with a performance of the Thousand Bagpipes March. The city is also host to the Edinburgh International Festival of Music

and Drama which takes place over three weeks in August.

In ancient times the Scottish clans gathered together to compete against each other in competitive games and sports. These gatherings are re-enacted every year at the Highland Games at Braemar. Here competitors engage in unique Scottish sports like hammer throwing and tossing the caber. The Highland Games are an

important social event, and are attended by members of the Royal Family. The Queen takes the clan salute at the Games, in her role as Chief of the clan chiefs. Perhaps the most important festival in the Scottish calendar is Hogmanay, on New Year's Eve. The Scots celebrate with food and drink, and at midnight it is customary to sing the folk song, Auld Lang Syne. [1]

Should old acquaintance
be forgot,
And never brought to
mind?
Should old acquaintance
be forgot,
And days of auld lang
syne?

1. **Auld Lang Syne** : literally 'old long since' referring to past times.

1 Match the following people with the castle to which they are associated.

PEOPLE	CASTLE
a. Macbeth	**1.** Balmoral
b. The Queen Mother	**2.** Cawdor
c. Queen Victoria	**3.** Glamis

2 What are the two important events that Edinburgh hosts every year?

3 What are two of the sporting events that take place at the Highland Games at Braemar?

4 Organise your own tour of Scotland. Try to obtain original material (dossiers, travel brochures, maps, and so on). Submit your itinerary of the places which would particularly interest you.

5 Scotland has been the setting for many films. How many of these can you list?

PART SEVEN

The Queen

Everyone began to talk of the army that was coming from England to Scotland. Everyone knew that Seyward was leading the army. Macbeth was determined to fight his enemies, and he collected his own army.

At Macbeth's castle there were strange rumours [1] about Macbeth's Queen. Some people said the Queen had gone mad, while others said that she was very ill. There was always a doctor with her.

One day one of the Queen's servants came to the doctor.

'There is something very wrong with the Queen,' she said. 'She walks in her sleep. If you watch with me tonight, you will see something very strange.'

The doctor and the servant waited in the corridor outside the Queen's room that night.

---

1. **rumours** : stories.

Macbeth

'She will come soon,' the servant said. 'She always comes at this hour of the night. I've seen her many times.'

Just then they heard a noise from the Queen's room and the door opened. Macbeth's wife came out.

'You see,' the servant said. 'She's walking, but she's asleep.'

'But she's doing something,' the doctor said. 'She seems to be rubbing her hands.' [1]

'She always does that,' the servant told him. 'It's as if she were washing her hands. I've seen her do that before.'

The Queen began to speak to herself.

'I'll clean these hands – I must clean these hands – Don't be afraid, Macbeth – No one will know it was us – What a lot of blood Duncan has!'

The doctor was very excited. He touched the servant's arm.

'Did you hear that?' he whispered. 'I wonder what that means.'

The Queen went on talking in her sleep.

'Macduff had a wife – Where is she now? – These hands of mine, they'll never be clean.'

'One thing is certain,' the servant said to the doctor. 'She has done terrible things, this Queen of ours.'

'I can't help her,' the doctor said. 'She is ill in the mind, and I can do nothing to help her.'

'She will soon go to bed,' the servant said.

The Queen continued to look at her hands. Then she spoke again.

'Banquo is dead – He can't hurt you – My hands! My hands – Who will wash my hands?'

Then the Queen returned to her room.

The doctor thought about what he had seen.

'It's true that she seems mad,' he thought, 'but her madness makes her

---

1. **rubbing her hands** : moving one hand against the other.

'"I'll clean these hands – I must clean these hands – Don't be afraid, Macbeth – No one will know it was us – What a lot of blood Duncan has!"'

tell the truth about the things she and Macbeth have done. They must have some terrible secrets!'

Macbeth waited for the enemy. Every day more of his men deserted him, but Macbeth did not care.

'Cowards! [1] Let them go,' he thought. 'The soldiers who remain only obey me because they are frightened of me. This is the last battle I will fight. I am tired of my life. I have no friends.'

Then he remembered the words of the witches:

'No man of woman born can hurt Macbeth.'

'Ah!' he said to himself. 'I'm not frightened of any man – Macduff can't defeat me. What else did the witches tell me? Now I remember:

'Macbeth will never be defeated until
Birnam Wood to Dunsinane Hill marches against him.'

'That's it!' he thought. 'I'll take my army to Dunsinane Hill – I can't be defeated there. There is still hope. I am ready to fight now.'

---

1. **cowards** : people without courage.

Comprehension

1 **Answer the following questions.**

   a. What were the rumours about Macbeth's wife?

   b. What does the servant ask the doctor to do?

   c. What does the doctor think about Macbeth's wife?

   d. Why does Macbeth still want to fight?

Vocabulary

2 **There are ten words relating to the medieval world in the word square. Find them and circle them.**

A	S	W	Y	B	I	E	T	S	X	C	E	Z	T	C
Q	Y	I	F	T	R	L	S	O	U	K	Y	T	I	A
R	E	G	H	E	U	T	O	W	I	T	C	H	E	S
K	I	N	G	T	W	T	L	K	O	B	D	A	W	T
H	J	G	E	S	U	A	D	T	Q	R	O	N	I	L
K	A	Y	O	M	E	B	I	R	U	F	D	E	G	E
D	Q	O	R	T	I	D	E	F	E	A	T	R	U	Z
W	U	N	L	I	M	E	R	J	E	S	A	D	R	T
B	O	C	T	N	F	U	S	X	N	W	Y	K	F	O

Grammar

In the text you read:

'**If** you **watch** with me tonight, you **will** see something very strange.'

This is the 1st conditional, and is used when we talk about a real possibility in the future. Remember that the verb in the 'if' clause is in the present tense.

3 **Choose the sentence below which best expresses the speaker's meaning above.**

   a. It's impossible that you watch with me tonight and see something very strange.
   b. It's unlikely that you will watch with me tonight, and therefore you will not see something very strange.
   c. Provided that you watch with me tonight, you will see something very strange.

4 **Complete the sentences.**

   a. If the witches .... *(be)* right Macbeth .... *(never be)* defeated.
   b. If the Queen .... *(continue)* talking in her sleep everyone .... *(know)* her secret.
   c. If Macduff .... *(fight)* Macbeth he .... *(kill)* him.
   d. If Duncan's son .... *(go)* back to Scotland everybody .... *(want)* him to be king.

Listening

 5 After you listen to Part Seven of *Macbeth* on the cassette you will hear a short extract from the original Shakespeare. Before you listen fill in the gaps with the words from the box. Then listen and check your answers.

> Arabia   blood   wife   known   Heaven   hands

Lady Macbeth: The Thane of Fife had a ....; where is she now? What, will these .... ne'er be clean? No more o' that, my lord, no more o' that. You mar ¹ all with this starting. ²

Doctor: Go to, ³ go to: you have .... what you should not.

Servant: She has spoke what she should not, I am sure of that. .... knows what she has known.

Lady Macbeth: Here's the smell of the .... still. All the perfumes of .... will not sweeten ⁴ this little hand. Oh! Oh! Oh!

Writing

6 Why do you think Lady Macbeth went mad? Was it a punishment for her crimes? Was there another reason?

Speaking

7 'All crimes can be forgiven.' Do you think this is true? Or do you think there are some crimes that can never be forgiven?

1. **mar** : ruin, destroy.
2. **starting** : surprise.
3. **Go to** : That's enough.
4. **sweeten** : make clean.

PART EIGHT

Birnam Wood to Dunsinane Hill

Seyward's army marched steadily [1] with Malcolm and Macduff towards Macbeth's castle. They stopped when they reached Birnam Wood. Malcolm was in charge of some of the soldiers, and he gave them their orders.

'Every soldier must cut a branch [2] from one of these trees,' he said. 'When we advance towards Dunsinane Hill, we will carry the branches in front of us. That way, no one will know how many of us there are. It will confuse Macbeth's army.'

The soldiers began to cut down branches from the trees in Birnam Wood. Inside the castle Macbeth sat alone. No one wanted to be with him.

1. **steadily** : without stopping.

2. **branch** :

Birnam Wood to Dunsinane Hill

Suddenly he heard a cry, and then the sound of women screaming.

A servant ran into the room.

'What is the noise?' asked Macbeth.

'The Queen is dead, sir,' the servant replied.

'She dies today,' said Macbeth. 'Today, when there is a battle to fight.' He sighed deeply. 'I don't have any time to think of her today.'

As Macbeth spoke, a messenger entered the room.

'Well, what is it?' asked Macbeth. 'What's the news?'

'I don't know how to tell you, sir,' the messenger said. 'I have seen something that I don't understand.'

'What did you see? Tell me quickly!' ordered Macbeth.

'I was standing on the castle wall,' said the messenger. 'As I looked out towards Birnam Wood, the wood seemed to move.'

'You're lying – it's impossible!' shouted Macbeth. Suddenly he was afraid.

'You can see for yourself, sir,' the messenger said. 'Birnam Wood is moving towards Dunsinane Hill.'

'Then I am finished,' Macbeth said to himself. 'Birnam Wood has come to Dunsinane Hill!' He thought for a moment, then he made a decision. 'If I am going to die today, I will at least die like a man. I'll die in battle.' He dressed himself in armour, [1] and went out to meet the enemy.

As Macbeth went out to the battle, one thought encouraged him.

'There is one hope,' he told himself. 'None of my enemies can kill me. The witches told me that I can't be killed by any man born of woman.'

Macbeth fought against the English army with courage. In the middle of the fighting Seyward's son came up to him. The young man challenged [2] him.

'Who are you?' he cried fiercely. [3]

1. **armour** :
2. **challenged** : asked him to fight.
3. **fiercely** : aggressively.

Macbeth

'You will be afraid to hear my name,' Macbeth told him. 'I am Macbeth.

'I hate that name,' the young man told him.

'Maybe you do hate it,' Macbeth replied. 'But you fear it, too. You are afraid of me, and you are right to be afraid of me. No one can kill me.'

'I am not afraid,' the young Seyward replied.

They took out their swords, and began to fight. Macbeth killed the young man. He looked down at the young man's body.

'You could not hurt me,' he thought. 'You were born of woman.'

As the battle continued, it became clear that the English army was winning. Macbeth's soldiers were killed and his castle was taken.

'What now?' he asked himself. 'My army is gone, and my castle is taken. What can I do?'

At that moment Macduff appeared.

'I have been searching for you!' he cried. 'You killed my wife and

Macbeth

children, and now I'm going to kill you!'

Macduff raised his sword, and moved towards Macbeth.

'Keep away from me,' Macbeth warned him. 'You can't kill me. No man born of woman can kill me. Run, and save yourself!'

Macduff looked at his enemy.

'Know this, Macbeth!' he shouted. 'I was not born of woman – I was taken early from my mother's womb. ¹ Prepare to die!'

'The witches played with me!' Macbeth thought. 'Everything they said was true, but it was all a trick. I believed them, and now I am defeated.'

He turned to Macduff.

'I won't fight you,' he said.

'You must surrender ² then,' Macduff told him. 'You will be our prisoner, and everyone will come to mock ³ you.'

'No!' cried Macbeth. 'I won't surrender. I won't be mocked by the people. Everything is lost. Birnam Wood has come to Dunsinane Hill, and you are not of woman born. Still, I prefer to fight. If I must die, I want to die like a king.'

Macbeth and Macduff fought together with their swords. Macduff killed the murderer of his wife and children. He cut off Macbeth's head, and put it on the end of his sword. Then he carried it to Malcolm.

'I have brought you the traitor's head, Your Majesty,' he said. 'You will be the new King of Scotland.'

1. **womb** [wuːm] : uterus.
2. **surrender** : stop fighting.
3. **mock** : make fun of.

Comprehension

1 **Answer the following questions.**

    a. What did Malcolm tell the soldiers to do when the army reached Birnam Wood?

    b. What news did the servant give Macbeth?

    c. Macbeth says that he has 'one hope' – what is it?

    d. Who does Macbeth kill in the battle?

    e. 'The witches played with me!' What does Macbeth mean by this statement?

Vocabulary

2 **Complete the sentences below with an appropriate word from the text.**

    a. Macbeth put on his .... before the battle.

    b. Macduff told him to fight or to ....

    c. Macduff told Macbeth that the people would .... him.

    d. Macbeth was a .... because he killed the King.

    e. Macbeth should not have believed what the .... told him.

3 **The words on the left come from the text. Match them with their synonyms on the right.**

a.	battle	**1.**	frightened
b.	messenger	**2.**	encounter
c.	servant	**3.**	fight
d.	enemy	**4.**	attendant
e.	afraid	**5.**	adversary
f.	meet	**6.**	courier

A C T I V I T I E S

Grammar

Present Perfect

We use the Present Perfect to refer to an action which began in an undefined past, and continues up to the present or when a finished event or action has consequences in the present.

You read in the text:

'I **have seen** something that I don't understand.'

This means that the speaker saw something at some undefined moment in the past and is still unable to make sense of what he saw.

4 **Practise making sentences of this type.**

   a. I .... English television because I .... the language. *(understand / study)*

   b. 'Why .... she in hospital?' 'She .... her leg.' *(be / break)*

   c. There .... nothing for lunch because the dog .... the meat. *(be / eat)*

   d. Mr Smith .... in the office – he .... out for lunch. *(not be / go)*

The Present Perfect Continuous shares the same time period as the Present Perfect. However its use indicates that an action began in the past and is still going on, or has just stopped. The action still has consequences in the present like the Present Perfect Simple, but the use of the continuous form indicates that the action has been in progress for a period of time and emphasises the continuation of action. Remember that certain verbs cannot be used in the continuous form.

You read in the text:

At that moment Macduff appeared.
'I **have been searching** for you!' he cried.

In which of the sentences in exercise 4 can we use the Present Perfect Continuous?

90

5 Look at the sentences below, and complete them with a verb in the Present Perfect Continuous. The verbs are in the box.

> wait   spend   work   make   study

a. 'You look tired, John.' 'I am tired, I .... all day.'

b. I am annoyed with the children. They .... a noise all afternoon.

c. I don't think he has any money. He .... a lot recently.

d. I think he will do well in the exam at school. He .... very hard.

e. You're late! I .... for two hours.

6 Fill in the gaps in the following sentences with a verb in either the Present Perfect Simple or the Present Perfect Continuous tense.

a. George is really hungry. He .... all day. *(not eat)*

b. I want to go home. I .... since early this morning. *(work)*

c. I can help you with your geography project. I .... to France. *(be)*

d. My son needs a holiday. He .... too hard. *(study)*

Listening

 7 After you listen to Part Eight of *Macbeth* on the cassette you will hear a short extract from the original Shakespeare. Before you listen try and fill in the gaps with the words from the box. Then listen and check your answers.

> more   name   hell   woman
> devil   afraid   fear   hateful

Macbeth: What's he

   That was not born of ....? Such a one

   Am I to ...., or none.

Young Seyward: What is thy [1] name?

---

1. **thy** : your.

Macbeth: Thou'lt [1] be ....to hear it.

Young Seyward: No: though thou call'st [2] thyself a hotter ....

Than any is in ....

Macbeth: My name's Macbeth.

Young Seyward: The .... himself could not pronounce a title [3]

More .... to mine [4] ear.

Macbeth: No, nor .... fearful. [5]

Writing

8 Write a short summary of the play.

Speaking

9 Imagine that you have been asked to act in a performance of *Macbeth.* Which role would you like to play, and why?

1. **thou'lt** : you will.
2. **call'st** : call.
3. **title** : name.
4. **mine** : my.
5. **fearful** : frightening.

Lines from Shakespeare

 10 After the bells, you will hear some famous lines from Shakespeare's original play. Remember that Shakespeare wrote 400 years ago, so the language is old-fashioned and sometimes difficult! Which character is speaking? Can you decide at which moment in the story the lines occur?

1. When shall we three meet again?
   In thunder, lightning, or in rain?

2. What are these,
   So withered [1] and so wild in their attire [2]
   That look not like th'inhabitants o'th'earth
   And yet are on't?

3. Glamis thou art, and Cawdor, and shalt be
   What thou art promised. Yet do I fear thy nature:
   It is too full o'the milk of human-kindness
   To catch the nearest way.

4. He's here in double trust:
   First, as I am his kinsman, and his subject,
   Strong both against the deed: then, as his host,
   Who should against his murderer shut the door,
   Not bear the knife myself.

5. Thou hast it now King, Cawdor, Glamis, all
   As the weird sisters promised, and I fear
   Thou played'st most foully for't; yet it was said
   It should not stand [3] in thy posterity, [4]
   But that myself should be the root [5] and father
   Of many kings.

6. Thou canst not say I did it; never shake
   Thy gory locks [6] at me.

7. Macbeth shall never vanquished [7] be, until
   Great Birnam Wood to high Dunsinane Hill
   Shall come against him.

---

1. **withered** : dry and old.
2. **attire** : clothes.
3. **stand** : remain.
4. **posterity** : descendants.

5. **root** : foundation.
6. **gory locks** : hair covered with blood.
7. **vanquished** : conquered.

8. Out damned spot! out, I say! [...] Yet who would have thought the old man to have had so much blood in him?

9. Bring me no more reports let them fly all:
   Till Birnam Wood remove to Dunsinane
   I cannot taint [1] with fear.

10. Let fall thy blade [2] on vulnerable crests, [3]
    I bear a charmèd [4] life, which must not yield [5]
    To one of woman born.

Discussion Questions

1 One of the themes of Macbeth concerns the nature of personal responsibility. Critics have argued about who is really responsible for the murder of King Duncan. Who do you think is most responsible?

RESPONSIBILITY

WITCHES They predict that Macbeth will become king.

Do they make their prediction to test Macbeth?

MACBETH He commits the murder.

Would he have committed the murder without the witches?

Would he have committed the murder without Lady Macbeth's encouragement?

LADY MACBETH She knows that her husband is ambitious but that he does not want to be 'cruel'.

She plans the murder of Duncan, and encourages Macbeth to carry it out.

Does the play help you to arrive at your own definition of 'personal responsibility'?

1. **taint** : change colour.
2. **blade** : sword.
3. **crests** : heads.
4. **charmèd** : protected by magic.
5. **yield** : surrender.

2 Another of the themes of the play concerns the nature of courage. At the beginning of the play Macbeth is described as being a brave man in battle: but there are moments in the play when he seems afraid. How does he behave in the following situations?

   a. When Lady Macbeth tells him of her plan to kill Duncan?

   b. Just before the murder?

   c. Just after the murder?

   d. At the end of the play, when he realises that he is going to be killed?

In your opinion, what does courage consist of?

3 Many critics have pointed out that the positions of Macbeth and Lady Macbeth become reversed throughout the play. Can you find evidence of this reversal of positions in what you have read? Compare the following scenes:

   a. Macbeth's vision of the dagger before the murder – Lady Macbeth's vision of the blood on her hands towards the end of the play.

   b. Macbeth telling his wife that he cannot kill Duncan because the King is his guest – the murder of Banquo after inviting him to the feast.

4 Another of the play's themes concerns the way that Macbeth's crime isolates him from 'nature' and human affection. Can you find evidence for this gradual isolation of Macbeth in the text you have read? You may find it helpful to consider the following:

   a. The relationship between Macbeth and his wife. Does this change throughout the play? Is there any sign that Macbeth keeps secrets from his wife? How does Macbeth react to the news of his wife's death?

   b. The relationship between Macbeth and Banquo. How does this change before Banquo's murder?

   c. The relationship between Macbeth and the thanes. How does this change throughout the play?

5 Another of the play's themes is about the nature of remorse and conscience. Macbeth and his wife do not acknowledge their guilt in words, but both of them see or hear things that symbolise their guilt. Macbeth sees the dagger before the murder, and he hears the voice that says 'Macbeth shall sleep no more' after the murder. He also sees Banquo's ghost. Lady Macbeth sees the blood on her hands. Do you think the audience is meant to believe in the 'reality' of these phenomena, or do they serve another purpose?

Macbeth

Playscript

Act One

It is the evening after the battle against the Thane of Cawdor and the King of Norway. Banquo and Macbeth are walking together.

BANQUO : We won, my friend. The King will be pleased with us. You were very brave today.

MACBETH : The Thane of Cawdor is defeated. We have done well.

Banquo sees the three witches. He points excitedly.

BANQUO : Look over there. Who are you? Are you women, or are you spirits?

FIRST WITCH : Welcome, Macbeth, Thane of Glamis.

MACBETH : How do you know who I am?

SECOND WITCH : Welcome, Macbeth, Thane of Cawdor.

MACBETH : Thane of Cawdor? – I'm not the Thane of Cawdor.

THIRD WITCH : Welcome, Macbeth, King of Scotland.

BANQUO : You tell my friend he will be Thane of Cawdor, and then King of Scotland. What about me? What is my future?

FIRST WITCH : You will be less than Macbeth, but more than Macbeth.

SECOND WITCH : You will be less lucky than Macbeth, but you will be more fortunate.

THIRD WITCH : You will never be king, but you will be the father of kings.

The three witches suddenly disappear.

MACBETH : How strange! They said I would be Thane of Cawdor, and then king – and you will be the father of kings! I don't know who they are, but I don't believe what they said. It makes no sense.

Ross now enters. He is looking for Macbeth.

ROSS : I have come from King Duncan. I have a message for you, Macbeth. The King is very pleased with you, and he wants to reward you. You will be the new Thane of Cawdor.

BANQUO : Thane of Cawdor!

MACBETH : The witches told the truth!

BANQUO : Be careful, my friend. Remember they also said you would be king. That's not possible. Perhaps they are bad spirits. I have heard that bad spirits try to make men do bad things by making them promises.

Act Two

Macbeth's castle. Lady Macbeth is reading the letter from her husband.

LADY MACBETH : 'Prepare everything for Duncan's visit. We must talk about what the witches told me. Thane of Cawdor, then King of Scotland – what can it mean?' It's a great chance for us, that's what it is. But I know you, Macbeth. You'd like to be the king, but you don't want to do anything bad. Come home, my love – I'll make you full of courage!

Macbeth's castle. Lady Macbeth is talking to her husband about Duncan's visit.

LADY MACBETH : You must act very cheerfully and innocently during the King's visit. Leave everything to me – Duncan will never leave the castle alive.

MACBETH : We cannot kill the King! He's been a good friend to me, and I can't murder him.

LADY MACBETH : Why did you tell me about the three witches, then? Don't you want to be king? Are you just frightened? Be brave, and you can have the throne!

MACBETH : But if we fail? What happens to us if we fail?

LADY MACBETH : Don't worry about that. We won't fail. I've got a plan. Duncan's room is guarded by two soldiers. I'll make sure that they drink a lot of wine. They won't know what's happening. It will be easy for you to go into the King's room and kill him. We can blame the soldiers for the murder.

MACBETH : You're right! No one will think it was us.

It is late at night in the castle. Macbeth comes out of the two soldiers' room. He is holding a knife, and his hands are covered in blood. He looks frightened. Lady Macbeth is waiting for him.

LADY MACBETH : Well? Did you do it?

MACBETH : Duncan is dead. I have done a terrible thing. Afterwards, I heard a voice. It said, 'There will be no more sleep. Macbeth has murdered sleep'. It was a frightening voice.

LADY MACBETH : Did it say anything else?

MACBETH : Yes. It cried out, 'Macbeth has murdered sleep – Macbeth will never sleep again'. It was a loud voice. I thought everyone in the castle would hear it.

LADY MACBETH : You're like a child! There was no voice, it was just your fear you heard. But the knife – why are you still carrying the knife? Go and put it in the soldiers' room!

MACBETH : I can't go back in there – I'll never go back in there!

LADY MACBETH : Give the knife to me. I'm not afraid. I'll put it in the soldiers' room.

Lady Macbeth goes into the soldiers' room. Macbeth is alone. He is looking at the blood on his hands.

MACBETH : I have done a terrible thing. This blood will never go away. I wish I hadn't done it!

Lady Macbeth comes back from the soldiers' room. Her hands are covered with blood.

LADY MACBETH : Look at my hands. They're red like yours – but I'm not afraid like you! A little water will remove the traces of our crime.

Act Three

Macduff and Lennox have just entered the castle. It is very early in the morning. They have made a noise, and woken up the porter. Macbeth comes down to see what is happening.

MACDUFF : Did you go to bed late, my friend? Perhaps you drank too much before you went to bed. Is that why you didn't hear the knocking on the gate?
PORTER : It's true, sir. I did drink too much last night.
MACDUFF : Good morning, Macbeth. Is the King awake yet?
MACBETH : He's still sleeping. Shall I wake him for you?
MACDUFF : I'll wake him myself. He asked me to come early this morning.

Macduff goes to the King's room. Macbeth and Lennox talk.

LENNOX : What a terrible night! The wind blew fiercely all night. Our chimneys were blown down. Some people said that they heard horrible screams.
MACBETH : It was just bad weather. It didn't mean anything.

They hear Macduff shouting from the King's room.

LENNOX : What is it? What's the matter? Is it the King?

Macduff comes from the King's room.

MACDUFF : It's dreadful, too dreadful. Go and look for yourselves.

MACBETH : Come on!

Macbeth and Lennox run off to the King's room.

MACDUFF : Murder! Murder! Sound the alarm!

People come from everywhere when they hear the shouting and the alarm. Enter Lady Macbeth, Malcolm and Donalblain. Macduff goes up to Malcolm and Donalblain.

LADY MACBETH : What is it? Why is there such a noise?

MACDUFF : There is terrible news.

MALCOLM : Tell us. Is it the King?

DONALBLAIN : What about our father?

MACDUFF : He's been murdered!

Macbeth and Lennox come down from the King's room.

MACBETH : It's true – Duncan has been murdered.

MALCOLM : Who did it? Who killed the King?

LENNOX : It was the two soldiers. When we went into their room, they were
   sleeping. They were covered in blood. We asked them questions, but they
   couldn't answer. It must have been them who killed Duncan.

MACDUFF : But why? Why would they do it? We must ask them why.

MACBETH : We can't ask them anything. When I saw them covered in the
   King's blood I killed them. I'm sorry. I shouldn't have done it. But I loved
   the King.

MACDUFF : Now we'll never know why they did it, or if someone paid them to
   do the murder.

LADY MACBETH : Oh, the King! The poor King! What a terrible thing to happen
   here, in my house. Who could have done it?

Lady Macbeth falls to the floor.

MACDUFF : The shock is too great for her. Help her, someone.

Macbeth picks up his wife, and helps her away.

BANQUO : Let's meet back here in one hour – we need to plan what to do about the King's murder.

Everybody leaves, except Malcolm and Donalblain.

DONALBLAIN : I don't feel safe here. Someone has murdered our father, and I don't believe what Macbeth told us.

MALCOLM : I don't believe Macbeth, either. Why would the two soldiers kill the King? It doesn't make any sense. We'll never really know what happened.

DONALBLAIN : Macbeth killed them too quickly.

MALCOLM : What do you mean?

DONALBLAIN : Macbeth said he killed the soldiers because he was angry. I don't think he was angry – I think he killed them because he didn't want them to be able to answer our questions!

MALCOLM : You suspect Macbeth?

DONALBLAIN : I don't know. But I think we should get away from this castle. Whoever killed our father is still here – and he may try to kill us next.

MALCOLM : I agree. I'll go to England. I've got friends there.

DONALBLAIN : And I'll go to Ireland.

Malcolm and Donalblain leave. Banquo, Macduff and the others come back.

MACDUFF : It must have been Malcolm and Donalblain who killed Duncan. They've run away from the castle. I think I know what happened. They paid the two soldiers to kill the King. They wanted the throne for themselves. We must make sure they suffer for this terrible crime!

BANQUO : Who shall we have as the new king?

MACDUFF AND THE OTHERS : Macbeth! Let's make Macbeth the new king! He was Duncan's friend.

Act Four

MACBETH : There is a feast tonight at the castle. You will be the guest of honour, my friend.

BANQUO : I will be there.

MACBETH : Bring your son Fleance with you – he's invited as well.

BANQUO : We will both be there. We are riding out this afternoon, but we will be at the castle tonight for the feast.

MACBETH : Tomorrow we must talk. I hear that Malcolm and Donalblain have gone to England and Ireland. They are trying to make trouble for me. We must decide what to do about them.

Banquo goes away, and Lady Macbeth joins Macbeth.

LADY MACBETH : You never seem happy, my love.

MACBETH : I am worried – I have enemies, you know.

LADY MACBETH : Tonight you must try to be cheerful at the feast. Remember that!

MACBETH : Tonight I will be cheerful, I promise.

LADY MACBETH : Forget the past. What we did, we did. We can't change anything now.

MACBETH : Sometimes I worry about Banquo and Fleance. I don't feel safe when I think of them.

LADY MACBETH : What can we do about them?

MACBETH : I have already done something – it's better that you don't know the details!

Outside the castle that evening. Three men are hiding in the darkness.

FIRST MURDERER : Are you sure Banquo and Fleance will come this way?

SECOND MURDERER : They'll come this way.

THIRD MURDERER : And when they do, we'll kill them both. Macbeth wants them to die.

FIRST MURDERER : Here they are! I can hear them.

Banquo and Fleance enter. The murderers attack Banquo.

THIRD MURDERER : Now!

SECOND MURDERER : Attack!

BANQUO : Ride, Fleance, ride! It's a trap!

Macbeth's castle, at the feast.

MACBETH : Welcome – I'm happy to see you all. Tonight we will enjoy ourselves with food and wine.

Enter the first murderer. Macbeth approaches him.

MACBETH : Well? How did it go?

FIRST MURDERER : Banquo is dead.

MACBETH : And Fleance? Tell me that Fleance is dead as well!

FIRST MURDERER : Fleance escaped us. He is free.

MACBETH : Then I'm not safe, after all. Go – there is blood on your face. We'll talk tomorrow.

LENNOX : Will Your Majesty sit with us?

MACBETH : Where shall I sit? All the chairs are taken.

LENNOX : There is an empty chair next to me.

Macbeth looks at the chair indicated by Lennox. He sees Banquo's ghost in the chair.

MACBETH : I didn't do it! Don't look at me like that. I didn't do it!

LENNOX : What's the matter with the King? Who is he talking to – that chair's empty!

LADY MACBETH : It is an illness of his. It will soon pass.

LADY MACBETH *(to her husband)* : What's the matter with you? Remember your guests. Where's your courage?

MACBETH *(to his wife)* : My courage! I'm a brave man to look at that ghost, and not run away!

LADY MACBETH *(to her husband)* : What ghost? There's nothing there. This ghost you see is like the knife you saw before you killed Duncan. It's your fear and your imagination.

MACBETH : But look at it! It's Banquo, can't you see?

The ghost disappears. Macbeth speaks to the guests.

MACBETH : Forgive me. It is an illness of mine. Let's drink to us. To us and to Banquo!

THE GUESTS : To us and to Banquo!

The ghost comes back into the room.

MACBETH : Why look at me? Away with you! Leave me alone!

THE GUESTS: What does the King mean? What is he looking at? What's wrong with him?

LADY MACBETH : The King is ill. He needs to rest.

The guests leave the room. Lady Macbeth and Macbeth are alone.

MACBETH : Macduff didn't come tonight. Why didn't he come?

LADY MACBETH : I don't know.

MACBETH : I don't trust any of them. They're all my enemies. I'll go back to the three witches. I must find out from them what is going to happen. Even if they tell me the worst, I must know!

Act Five

Macbeth with the three witches.

MACBETH : I have come here to ask you something. You must tell me the truth.

THIRD WITCH : If you don't trust us, our masters will come to answer your question. Would you prefer that?

MACBETH : Call your masters. I want to see them. Call them now.

The witches stir the contents of the cooking-pot. A head rises in the air in front of Macbeth.

MACBETH : Tell me –

THE WITCHES : Don't speak! He knows what you want.

THE HEAD : Macbeth, be careful of Macduff! That's my message, it's enough.

The head disappears. The witches stir the contents of the pot again, and a second spirit appears.

SECOND SPIRIT : Macbeth, be brave and laugh to scorn the power of man. No man of woman born can hurt Macbeth.

The second spirit disappears. The witches stir the pot once again, and a third spirit appears.

THIRD SPIRIT : Macbeth will never be defeated until Birnam Wood to Dunsinane Hill fights against him.

The third spirit disappears.

MACBETH : You have done well. But there is one thing more that I want to know. Will Banquo really be the father of kings?

ALL THE WITCHES : Ask no more! Ask no more!

MACBETH : I must have an answer – tell me the truth!

ALL THE WITCHES : Show the truth, and break his heart. Then we witches will depart.

The ghost of Banquo appears in front of Macbeth. He is surrounded by kings. The image stays for a moment, and then disappears. Macbeth puts his head in his hands. He is in despair.

Act Six

Two thanes are talking with Macduff about Macbeth.

FIRST THANE : I don't think Malcolm and Donalblain paid the two soldiers to
   kill their father. They loved him too much.

SECOND THANE : Why did they run away, then?

FIRST THANE : I think they were frightened.

SECOND THANE : What about the soldiers? Do you think they killed Duncan?

MACDUFF : I'll tell you what I think. I think the man who killed Duncan
   wanted to be king himself.

FIRST THANE : And Banquo? Who killed Banquo, I wonder? Do you think it was
   Macbeth?

MACDUFF : I don't know. But I don't feel safe here in Scotland. I'm going to
   England. Something is wrong in Scotland. We live in bad times.

   *England. Malcolm is trying to persuade Macduff to fight against
   Macbeth.*

MALCOLM : Will you fight with us? We need a man like you.

MACDUFF : I don't know. It's true that Macbeth is a bad man – but I am not a
   traitor. Give me time to think about it.

   Enter Ross.

MACDUFF : What's the news from Scotland?

ROSS : All the news from Scotland is bad. There is talk of a rebellion against
   Macbeth. We need you, Macduff.

MACDUFF : And my family – is my family all right?

ROSS : This is the worst news of all. Macbeth sent some men to your castle.
   They killed your wife.

MACDUFF : What about my children? Are my children safe?

ROSS : They killed everybody – your wife, your children, even the servants in
   the castle.

MACDUFF : Not my children! My little children dead!

MALCOLM : Now will you join us against Macbeth? We'll take an army into

Scotland. We'll defeat Macbeth!

MACDUFF : I'll come with you. I want to be the man who kills Macbeth – I want revenge!

Act Seven

Macbeth's castle. A woman servant is talking to Lady Macbeth's doctor.

SERVANT : There is something very wrong with the Queen. She walks in her sleep at night. I want you to watch with me tonight, to see what happens.

DOCTOR : The Queen appears.

SERVANT : There she is! She's walking, but she's asleep.

DOCTOR : What's she doing? She seems to be rubbing her hands.

SERVANT : She always does that. Is she washing her hands?

The Queen begins to speak to herself.

LADY MACBETH : I'll clean these hands – I must clean these hands – Don't be afraid, Macbeth – No one will know it was us – What a lot of blood Duncan has!

DOCTOR : Did you hear that? I wonder what it means.

LADY MACBETH : Macduff had a wife – Where is she now? – These hands of mine, they'll never be clean.

DOCTOR : I can't help her – she's mad.

LADY MACBETH : Banquo is dead – he can't hurt you – My hands! – Who will wash my hands?

SERVANT : She will soon go to bed.

DOCTOR : She is mad, but her madness tells the truth. Macbeth and his wife have done some terrible things. I wish I was away from this castle!

Act Eight

Seyward's army has arrived at Birnam Wood.

MALCOLM : Every soldier must cut a branch from one of these trees. We'll carry the branches in front of us, it will confuse Macbeth's army.

Inside Macbeth's castle. Macbeth with a servant.

MACBETH : What is the noise?

SERVANT : The Queen is dead, sir.

MACBETH : She dies today, when there is a battle to fight. I cannot think of her today.

A messenger enters the room.

MACBETH : Well, what is it? What's the news?

MESSENGER : I don't know how to tell you, sir. I have seen something that I don't understand.

MACBETH : What did you see? Tell me quickly.

MESSENGER : As I looked out towards Birnam Wood, the wood seemed to move.

MACBETH : You're lying – it's impossible!

MESSENGER : You can see for yourself, sir. Birnam Wood is moving towards Dunsinane Hill.

MACBETH : Then I am finished. Birnam Wood has come to Dunsinane Hill! But I will die like a man. Anyway, no man of woman born can kill me – it's my one hope.

The battle. Young Seyward sees Macbeth.

YOUNG SEYWARD : Who are you?

MACBETH : You will be afraid to hear my name. I am Macbeth.

YOUNG SEYWARD : I hate that name!

MACBETH : You fear it, too.

YOUNG SEYWARD : I am not afraid.

Macbeth and Young Seyward fight – Seyward is killed. Macduff approaches Macbeth.

MACDUFF : I have been searching for you. Today I will kill you!

MACBETH : Keep away from me! You can't kill me. No man born of woman can kill me. Run, and save yourself.

MACDUFF : Know this, Macbeth. I was not born of woman. I was taken early from my mother's womb. I'll kill you for the deaths of my wife and children.

MACBETH : I won't fight you!

MACDUFF : You must surrender, then. You will be our prisoner. Everyone will come to mock you.

MACBETH : No! I won't surrender. I won't be mocked by the people. Everything is lost. Birnam Wood has come to Dunsinane Hill, and you are not of woman born. Still, I prefer to fight.

Macbeth and Macduff fight. Macbeth is killed.

Notes

FICO